GOR
cn

REAL LIVES

Boudica

Boudica

Gaby Halberstam

A & C BLACK • LONDON

First published 2012 by
A & C Black, an imprint of Bloomsbury Publishing Plc
50 Bedford Square, London, WC1B 3DP

www.acblack.com
www.bloomsbury.com

Copyright © 2012 A & C Black
Text copyright © 2012 Gaby Halberstam

The right of Gaby Halberstam to be identified as the author
of this work has been asserted by her in accordance with
the Copyrights, Designs and Patents Act 1988.

ISBN 978-1-4081-3392-7

A CIP catalogue for this book is available from the British Library.

All rights reserved. No part of this publication may be
reproduced in any form or by any means – graphic, electronic or
mechanical, including photocopying, recording, taping or information
storage and retrieval systems – without the prior permission
in writing of the publishers.

This book is produced using paper that is made from wood grown in
managed, sustainable forests. It is natural, renewable and recyclable.
The logging and manufacturing processes conform to the
environmental regulations of the country of origin.

Printed and bound in Great Britain
by CPI Cox & Wyman, Reading RG1 8EX

1 3 5 7 9 10 8 6 4 2

Contents

1
Beaten

"Get your hands off me!" she screamed, jerking and tugging her arms to free herself. "You – you stinking Roman thugs!"

Bucking her head so that her long red hair whipped at their faces, and kicking, lunging and jack-knifing her body, Boudica struggled against the iron grip of the centurions on either side of her.

When her husband, King Prasutagus, had been alive, he'd exchanged loyalty to the Roman Emperor, Claudius, for peace in the kingdom of the Iceni. Now, it was the year 60. Claudius was dead, and her bold and clever husband was dead, too. And Nero had stepped into Claudius's sandals, and sent his cruel procurator to Britain to squeeze whatever he could out of its people, however he could.

From the back of her villa, Boudica heard piercing screams, joined by frantic shrieking.

Her daughters.

The Romans had captured both of her daughters, Tasca and Camorra.

Fear stabbed her stomach, sharp as a javelin blade. She'd told them to run, to get out of the villa, to hide. Why hadn't they listened to her? Why hadn't she sent them far away weeks ago, when Prasutagus died? She should have known the Romans would come for them.

"Help! Moth– " Tasca's voice was stifled.

Boudica lunged at the centurion on her left, her mouth open. She sank her teeth into his arm and kept her jaw locked.

"Briton she-devil!" the centurion yelled, flinging his arm to free it.

Boudica felt his skin tear as her head flew upwards. She spat. He jerked her away from him and tightened his grip.

"Let go! Take me to my daughters!" She jerked and elbowed and kicked, cursing and spitting.

The centurions looked straight ahead. They squeezed her arms and lifted her off the ground.

She arched her back and launched her feet at the centurion to her left, striking him with all the force of her anger. He flinched. She saw her chance. Slick as lightning, she delivered another kick. In the moment he took to register the pain, she was free of his grasp and clawing the other soldier.

"You – will – be – punished – for – this," she said through clenched teeth. "Nero – himself – will hear of this!" And with the first two fingers of her left hand outstretched, she lunged at the centurion's eyes.

"Watch it, woman!" He grabbed her hand, bent her arm behind her back and within seconds she found herself strung between the two soldiers, one holding her arms stretched behind her, the other gripping her feet.

"I'm not 'woman'!" she yelled. "I'm Boudica, Queen of the Iceni. Not some common slave!"

Just then a third centurion came running.

"Need help?" he asked.

"Shut her up, will you," one of the others said.

"A pleasure," he said, with a grunt. "The daughters were wild, too. One of them got me." He pointed to the deep scratch marks that raked his cheek.

Before Boudica could say another word, he grabbed her face and bound a strip of cloth tightly over her mouth and around the back of her head.

Her daughters. Where were they now? What had the soldiers done to them? She must get to them immediately. She began to thrash again, screaming through the cloth.

A sharp blow to her head turned everything dark and, after a thick rush of sound, completely silent.

It was a loud roar and a sharp, banging pain in her head that made her open her eyes. The light was harsh. She blinked. How long had she been unconscious? Trying to move, she found her hands and feet were tied, and the cloth was still tight across her mouth. The roar in her ears became the clamour of human voices. As her eyes adjusted to the bright sunlight, she found that she was lying at the edge of the marketplace. Around her the Iceni people – her people – were crowded, shouting and stamping their feet, dust billowing and filling her nostrils. She saw that they were held back by a wall of centurions, light flashing off their helmets.

"Lady! Help us! Why is this happening?"

"Help us, Queen Boudica!"

"This would never have happened when King Prasutagus was alive!"

Boudica struggled to get up. Immediately, the two centurions standing guard over her each grabbed one of her arms and dragged her upright.

A gasp ran through the crowd. Some surged forward, only to be beaten back by the soldiers.

"Let me go!" she shouted through the cloth over her mouth, flinging her head from side to side.

The centurions hauled her across the square, her toes scraping against the rough stones. She saw where they were taking her. Writhing and twisting, she tried again to free herself, but in no time they'd reached the stone column in the centre. Quickly, the soldiers untied her hands and flung her against it so that her chin bashed against the warm stone. Her hands were pulled round the column and tied once again.

"No!" the people shouted.

One of the centurions stepped forward and pressed her face hard against the stone. There was a rattle and a sharp rush of air. Boudica knew that he was flicking the flagrum, the whip the Romans loved so much.

She knew what would follow.

Stiffening her back, she clenched her fists. She did not have long to wait.

With a grunt, and all the strength in his huge arm, the centurion brought the flagrum down on her back. Boudica closed her eyes and focussed not on the pain, but on her determination for revenge. In the name of her dead husband, King Prasutagus, her daughters' honour and her proud and brave people, she would pay back these Roman dogs. Each burning stripe across her back meant a thousand Romans she would kill.

2

Death to the Romans!

At last, the centurion dealt his final lash. Despite the pain that rang through her back, pain that burned as if she had been branded with a flaming iron, Boudica had refused to cry out once. She wouldn't give the Romans that satisfaction.

The Roman flung his flagrum at her feet, the clumps of metal threaded along the leather thongs clattering as they hit the ground. She heard the soldiers leave, the drumming of their horses' hooves, the shouts of her people as they were beaten by passing centurions.

All at once, Boudica was exhausted. She slumped against the column, all the determination she'd summoned as the centurion flogged her now draining away. She pressed her cheek against it, just as she had pressed her face to her husband's body only weeks before. Oh, Prasutagus, she thought. Why did you have to die? A tear rolled from her eye, and quickly she smudged it against the stone.

As soon as he'd drawn his last breath, the wild Roman dogs had descended on his kingdom – grabbing and stealing and looting, unleashing their violence and brutality on the Iceni. Boudica had hoped to be able to speak to the Procurator, to persuade him to rein back his men. She'd failed.

The people were still gathered in the forum. The clamour that rose from them was full of despair and confusion. They needed someone to take control. The Iceni needed a new leader.

Then the thought came to her. Could she do it? A woman? After all, Prasutagus had insisted on showing her how to use a sword. He'd even shown Camorra and Tasca, which had made her uncomfortable. He'd hated leaving them on their own while he was away fighting.

So she was a woman who could wield a sword. So what? She was also a woman who, so far, had only been in charge of a household.

No. She could not do it. She could not lead

the Iceni into battle. She shut her eyes. The only commands she'd ever given were to her slaves to wash her feet.

"Lady!" She heard the shouting of the people. "Help us, Lady!"

Boudica wore the gold torc that her husband had always worn. She hadn't allowed it to grow cold with his body, but had fastened it, still warm from him, around her own neck. Now, its twisted gold bands felt hot against her skin, a circle of heat that forced her to open her eyes. Was it a sign? Was it a message from her beloved Prasutagus?

Boudica straightened up. The commander of the Brigantes tribe was a woman: if Queen Cartimandua could do it, then why not Boudica, Queen of the Iceni?

She took a deep breath.

"Untie me!" she ordered.

Two of her servants drew near. She could see that they found it difficult to look at her back.

"Untie me, I said! What? You are as timid as mice!" she shouted. "It is only flesh that has been broken, not my spirit."

Her hands free, slowly she raised herself to her

full height. Her hair was spattered and her tunic soaked with blood, but the gold torc round her neck shimmered in the sunlight.

"Iceni!" Her voice came out hoarse. "Iceni," she tried again. "You mourn – I mourn – our king, King Prasutagus."

The gathered crowd murmured. Some hung their heads, still heavy with grief.

"But do not fear, Iceni, for you are not without a leader in these times of trouble." Lifting her arms, she announced: "I, Boudica, shall lead you." She stepped into the crowd, striding through until she reached the middle. A gasp swept through the people as they saw how her skin had been damaged by the soldier's whip.

"They have stolen from us."

"Yes, Lady!" Some of the crowd began to shout.

"They have made us their slaves."

"Yes, Lady!" More and more people joined in, shouting and stamping their feet.

"They have attacked us, dishonoured us, disgraced us, beaten us –" Boudica's voice couldn't be heard for the roar of the Iceni. She raised her right arm high, and slowly they quietened. "So join me, my people. Let us not shrink with terror. Let us rise against them, and fight to free ourselves. Whatever they have made us suffer, they will suffer – and more." She clenched her hand into a fist and shook it. "Death to the Romans!"

"Death to the Romans!" The Iceni echoed Boudica's words, their voices joining together in one huge battle cry. "Death to the Romans!"

By nightfall, every Iceni man, woman and child had gathered in the heart of the forest of Thetford. Boudica moved from campfire to campfire, clan to clan, stopping to speak to her people. Her bold words encouraged them.

"We shall fight with you, Lady!" they said. "At your side, through thick and thin."

"We shall avenge your – and our – loss of honour!"

"Death to the Romans!" they repeated, brandishing the weapons they had brought with them.

Her heart warmed by the loyalty of her people, Boudica was able to ignore the fierce pain in her back as she made her way back to her encampment. At last, she reached her own campfire. Her daughters, Camorra and Tasca, were asleep beside each other, their long red hair tangled together. Camorra cried out, and quickly Boudica knelt to comfort her. Even by the dying embers of the campfire, she could see the bruises on their arms and the streaks their tears had made down their cheeks.

Boudica touched each of them softly on the head. The Romans would pay.

Too exhausted to undress, she lay down between her daughters, restless and sleepless, staring at the indigo night sky. *Am I doing the right thing, Prasutagus?* she wondered. *Do I have the strength and courage to see it through?*

Earlier that evening Boudica had despatched Iaros, her speediest messenger, to Camulodunum, the chief town of the Trinovantes. They were the neighbours of the Iceni, and from what she'd heard, they too were suffering at the hands of the Romans. She'd had an idea: if she could persuade Brennus, their commander, to join them, together the Iceni and the Trinovantes would be a fierce and unstoppable force that would mow the Romans down and teach them a lesson they would never forget. She took a deep breath, heartened by that thought.

The sky lightened. Still she could not sleep. She watched a kite soar and swoop overhead. From somewhere behind her, an owl hooted. Doubt now began to nag at her, and worry, too. How would Brennus receive her request that they meet? What if he refused? Worse – what if he betrayed her to the Romans?

She rose at dawn, her back burning with pain, and her bones stiff from her night on the ground. Her slave brought her a bowl of cold water from the stream. As she bent to splash her face, she heard the crack and rustle of branches and undergrowth, and the thud of footsteps. Immediately, she sprang to attention.

"Who goes there?" her guards yelled.

"Messenger," a youth replied, panting, his voice hoarse.

Boudica stepped forward. "Speak!" she ordered.

The guards grabbed his arms.

"Messenger. Envoy of Brennus, Commander of the Trinovantes."

Boudica signalled her men to let go of him. Was it good news or bad that he brought?

3
Alliance

"Speak!" she commanded again, planting herself in front of him. She towered over him.

The messenger's eyes widened. He turned his gaze away and shifted from one foot to the other. "Lady... Commander Brennus salutes you. He summons you to his camp at the edge of the Forest."

So he had travelled to meet her. Good news – probably. But she would not know for certain until they met. She considered the message: summoned to his camp? She shook her head.

"It is *I* who have summoned *him*," Boudica said, touching the gold torc at her neck. "Conduct your commander to our camp." She glanced at the sky. Dawn was already widening into day. "Now. I await his arrival."

She sent two Iceni guards with the messenger.

She did not have long to wait before their return. Standing with the rising sun behind her, she held her head high.

Brennus beat back the branches of the trees as he approached. He was tall, with wild, snarled-up blond hair hanging in long clumps over his huge shoulders and down his back.

"Greetings, Commander," Boudica said.

His beard was a thicket; bits of twig and leaves were trapped in it. In the middle of the mass of hair, his eyes glittered, small, sharp and eagle-fierce. A thick, red scar snaked across his face from his right eyebrow through his beard and down his neck. He raised his right hand in greeting. Two fingers were missing.

"You sent for me, your ladyship?" He bent in an exaggerated bow. Boudica knew he was mocking her. She would not have that.

"Straight to the point," Boudica said. "Will the Trinovantes fight the Romans side by side with the Iceni? What is your answer?"

Brennus pulled out the dagger that was stabbed through the leather of his belt. Still looking at her,

21

a smile playing round his mouth, he dug between his teeth with the edge of the blade.

"A woman like you – playing at war?" He jerked his head. "Go back to your villa. Have your slaves tend your hair. Play with your lapdogs."

The smirk on his face made Boudica want to strike him. Instead, she flung her hand out, dismissing him, and turned on her heel.

She heard his gasp as she turned her back.

"Wait!" Brennus shouted. "They did that to you? The Roman dogs did that? And you're still standing?"

Boudica stopped. Remembering that she'd not exchanged the blood-soaked tunic for a fresh one, she realised that it was that, and the damage to her back, that must have shocked Brennus. She smiled to herself before turning once again to face him.

No longer was Brennus so scornful. He shook his head in disbelief, a look of surprise and admiration in his eyes. "The look of a woman, the strength of a man," he muttered.

Boudica chose to ignore his comment. "I shall ask you once more, and only once," she said. "You Trinovantes – do you have the courage to join us in the fight against the Romans?"

Brennus's face reddened, and he set his jaw. "Those Roman dogs," he said, his lips curled into a snarl. "They abuse us. They oppress us. They steal, dishonour and violate. They have built a temple to their old emperor, Claudius, in our town." He spat. "We, the Trinovantes, we hate the Romans." Plunging the dagger back into his belt, he said, "I see you are a warrior, Queen Boudica, built in the mould of the Trinovantes. The answer is yes. My people will fight at the side of their Iceni comrades."

He stretched out his hand. Boudica shook it.

"Good," she said. "We must move quickly. This is my plan: advance on Camulodunum. Take the Romans by surprise. Kill each and every one of them."

Brennus gave a grudging smile. "I like your plan."

"Gather your warriors," Boudica said. "My people are ready. We shall depart immediately. Let us meet the Trinovantes at the walls of Camulodunum."

She took her mantle from her attendant and fastened it at the neck with the brooch that had been a gift from Prasutagus.

"To victory!" she shouted.

4
Omens

She gathered all her people, and led them through the forest to where the chariots were waiting. She helped her daughters into their chariot, before making for her own. It had been her husband's; its wheels were scarred with the marks of his many battles. There was a man standing beside it. He was small, his skin darkened by the weather, and his face seamed with wrinkles.

He stepped forwards.

"Lady," he said, dipping his head with its frizzled grey hair. "My name is Drustan. King Prasutagus was my master. Now I wish to serve you."

When he raised his head, Boudica found herself looking into eyes that were deep blue and fierce with loyalty.

"Thank you, Drustan," Boudica said. Prasutagus

had always praised him as a faithful servant and a skilful charioteer. She touched his arm lightly. It was good to have him by her side.

She leapt aboard the chariot, and Drustan followed. Then with her head held high and her red hair streaming behind her, she raised her hand.

"To Camulodunum!" she shouted, and with one smart crack of the whip, Drustan spurred the horses on.

With a jolt they were off: behind her were her massed people, some on horseback, most on chariots, the large wheels racing over the dry earth. The clash and clatter of their shields and spears and javelins, the high repeated call of the trumpets and the thud of the horses' hooves made Boudica's heart swell with pride, and thrill with excitement at the battle to come.

They were some miles from the Trinovantes' main town, Camulodunum, when Boudica spotted a small cloud of dust in the distance growing larger. Soon she made out three women running from the settlement, their hair wild, their mouths stretched wide open. They looked as though they'd seen the most terrible thing.

Boudica signalled the train of chariots to stop. Huge clouds of dust billowed as the chariots and horses thudded and clattered to a halt behind her.

"Ruined!" one of the women screamed, her voice shrill above the neighing and whinnying of the Iceni horses and the questioning calls of the people.

"Our people will be destroyed, totally destroyed!" another wailed, flinging herself to the ground. "We shall all die!"

"What is it, women?" she asked. "What has happened?"

Taking deep, heaving breaths, the third woman turned her face slowly to look up at Boudica. Her ash-coloured skin and the look of terror in her wide eyes were shocking.

"The statue of Victory – our statue – fallen," she said. "Fallen for no reason – lying on the ground, face turned away – as if giving in to our enemy."

"Oh," one of the other women cried, wringing her hands, "it is a horrible omen!" She plucked at the tunics of her companions. "Run! Flee! Before we are caught in the disaster that awaits our people in Camulodunum!"

Boudica frowned. She was alarmed to hear of the fallen statue. It was a bad sign, but it was not something that would stop her.

"Do not fear this omen," she said. "We, the Iceni, are here to help your people."

The women stood back, clinging to each other, but calmer now.

"We thank you, Lady," one of them said, dipping her head in a bow. "May the omens be good from now on."

Boudica raised her hand in thanks. She then signalled to Drustan to move on, and before long she could hear once again the thudding and shouting and clattering and trumpeting behind her.

A cheer rose from the Iceni when they smelled the tang of the sea, and caught sight of the glittering water far in the distance. But before they could draw near to the coast, the chariots had first to steer inland around the mouth of the Thames.

The Britons slowed their chariots at the banks of the river. The horses were hot and thirsty. Boudica leapt from her chariot to dip her hands in the clear, cold water. As she bent to splash the dust from her face, she felt a plucking at her mantle.

"Please, Lady."

A small dark-haired girl of about six was standing beside her.

"Come quickly," she said, her black eyes wide with fear. "It's Mother."

Boudica followed the girl through the throng of Iceni. There was a murmuring that grew louder as they approached a woman standing at the water's edge. She had her back to Boudica, but Boudica recognised her at once.

She was Genovefa. Broad-shouldered and square-jawed, she'd taken on her husband's blacksmith work after he'd been killed fighting alongside Prasutagus. She stood now, her arms stiff at her sides, her cheeks flushed bright red and a glassy look in her dark eyes that sent a shiver down Boudica's spine.

"Genovefa!" Boudica said loudly, hoping to stir the woman out of her trance. She placed her hand on Genovefa's shoulder, but she ignored it and turned back to the water.

The little girl began to sob. "Mother! Wake up, Mother!" she cried.

But Genovefa seemed not to hear her child nor

28

feel her frantic tugging at her tunic. Crouching at the water's edge, she peered into the clear waters.

"A colony... a Roman colony... in ruins..." she murmured, pointing.

Boudica knelt beside her. She stared into the depths of the river. She saw nothing besides weed fronds, small fish and the stony river bed.

"Is it – are you seeing some sort of image? A vision?" Boudica asked.

"Everything is broken. Knocked down," Genovefa said.

"Can anyone else see anything?" Boudica asked the people standing around them.

"No, Lady," they said, shaking their heads. "Nothing but fish and weeds."

Genovefa gasped. "Red plumes... rising from the colony," she said. "Crimson plumes of blood!"

The Iceni drew back in alarm. Boudica put her hand up to calm them.

Genovefa was not the kind of person who would make up such a thing. With her husband dead, and children to support, she'd had to learn the blacksmithing business quickly. Now she was as well known for her workmanship and trustworthiness as her husband had been. Yes, she was a sensible woman, strong and practical.

Boudica watched as Genovefa continued to stare at the water. Minutes passed. Slowly the tension in Genovefa's body loosened, and the flush in her cheeks faded. She stood up, stumbling a little. Boudica grabbed her elbow to steady her.

"It has gone now," Genovefa said quietly.

Her daughter ran to her side, and burrowed into her mother's tunic. Genovefa scooped her into her arms.

The gathered Iceni were silent. Boudica saw how frightened they were by Genovefa's vision, especially after hearing about the bad omen from the three women. But Boudica was not alarmed. Her spirit had leapt at what Genovefa described, and now she felt a huge surge of energy.

"My people," she addressed them, her voice loud and commanding. "Genovefa's vision is a good omen, not a bad one. It is a sign, a wonderful sign!"

Some of the Iceni cheered, joined by others as they saw how Boudica smiled.

"It is a sign of our victory over the Romans! The

image of destruction that Genovefa saw in these waters is a reflection of the damage that we shall bring upon our enemy."

She lifted her chin, flinging her head back so that her fiery mane of hair swung down her back, and the sun caught her husband's torc. Stretching her arms out to either side, her large hands open and facing upwards, she called upon the goddess Andraste and promised her a sacrifice before long.

A roar burst from the Iceni.

Her heart swelling with joy, Boudica grabbed the bronze carnyx, the special battle horn, from the hands of one of the men standing nearby. Leaping on board her chariot, she put the instrument to her lips and sounded twenty notes, each following quickly after the one before. The harsh call pierced the still air like the hoarse cries of a hunted animal, moments before death.

"To victory!" she shouted.

"To victory!" the Iceni echoed.

They daubed their skins with blue dye and re-mounted their chariots, the sounding of the horns and trumpets even more loud and jarring and stirring than before. Thundering round the mouth of the Thames, with the salt of the sea strong in their noses, they drew ever closer to Camulodunum.

5

Camulodunum

"Typical Roman welcome!" Boudica shouted to Drustan, pointing to the avenue of spikes on either side of the straight road into Camulodunum.

Many of the spikes were topped with cut-off heads. Some had been there a long time, white skulls gleaming through the dried-out skin. Others were fresh, with black crows clustered over the flesh, busily pecking out the eyes.

She gave a bitter laugh. "Well, we shall leave with Roman heads hanging from our horses!"

They approached the gateway to the town. Boudica ordered the chariots to slow. Shielding her eyes from the sun with one hand, she looked around. Where were the Trinovante warriors? No sign. The ground around the entrance to the town did not look as though it had been recently driven over by an army: there were no deep wheel ruts, and no half moon imprints of hundreds of horses' hooves.

That rogue, Brennus, she thought, frowning. *Dirty, double-crossing villain.* Smacking the edge of the chariot, she cursed herself for trusting him.

"What is it, Lady?" Drustan asked, glancing across at her.

Fingering the torc, she shook her head. There was no point in drawing him into the worry that was nagging her. Something was wrong. She signalled for the train of chariots to stop, and ordered her people to be silent.

Without the rumble and creak of the chariots and the call of the horns, the air was still. Only the buzz of the flies pestering the horses broke the quiet.

Boudica felt her stomach clench.

That was the problem: the quiet.

Was she leading her people into a trap?

"Wait here," she ordered Drustan.

Signalling all the chariots to remain where they were, too, she leapt down from her chariot. Alone she made her way down the main street into

Camulodunum, looking to the left and right as she walked.

"Strange," she muttered. "There's no sign of any Roman soldiers, or any defence whatsoever." She had expected to see trenches dug at the very least, as well as some sort of camp. The fact that there were no signs of an army was worrying.

The streets were empty. The town looked abandoned. Normally there'd be children playing outside, people meandering or scurrying about, beggars crouching on street corners, hands outstretched. Only a mangy dog slunk out of an alley and came to sniff at her feet for a moment. Although the town seemed deserted, Boudica felt uneasy: she felt as though she were being watched. The thought made her skin prickle. She kept going until she reached a small square.

"By Andraste!" she exclaimed. "So it *is* true."

Across the flagstones, the statue of Victory lay just as the three women had said, separated from its base, its head turned to the side. Not a good omen.

But Boudica gave it no more than a glance, as from the forum ahead of her, she'd heard the scuff and thud of footsteps. There were people about.

Romans or Trinovantes?

Was she walking into an ambush?

Better that she find out on her own than lead her people into it. Whoever was there would not know who she was. If someone stopped her, she could always pretend to be a lost traveller who'd stumbled into the town, or a madwoman. Despite the butterflies flickering in her stomach, she quickened her pace.

Keeping to the shadows, she slipped into the forum. Her back to a wall, she scanned the stone faces of the basilica and the bath house and the temple. *Ah,* she thought, the Romans' temple to Claudius. It dominated the other buildings, like an ox amongst chickens. No wonder the Trinovantes were so angry.

All was silent. Perhaps she'd been mistaken about the footsteps. There was no one about.

With a loud flap of wings, a lone pigeon flew from the pedestal above the temple. Startled, Boudica leapt backwards. Just then a group of people ran from an open doorway in the far corner of the forum. Romans. They ran for the temple, heads down, darting between its pillars and into the entrance. Boudica stayed where she was, wondering. A few minutes later, another twelve or thirteen followed. And then a few more, all rushing into the temple, not looking left or right.

Who were they running from? And why were they all making for the temple?

Two Roman women scuttled out from the doorway, one of them clutching to her chest a baby swaddled in linen, the other dragging a small child. "Quick, Faustina!" the one with the toddler hissed. The women darted looks around them, looking over their shoulders. Boudica strained to hear what she said next. She caught only the words "hide" and "barbarians".

With a smile, Boudica turned away from the forum. Light on her feet, she ran back through the streets, back to where her chariot and her people were waiting. Leaping aboard once more, she turned to the Iceni.

"I don't know where the Trinovante warriors are," she said. "The town is silent. But I've seen something that has made my heart bold." She laughed. "Like rats," she said, making scuttling movements with her fingers. "Like rats, the Romans are running out of their hiding places. They're running to their temple – the very temple that has so angered the Trinovantes. They're hiding there, shivering with fear. Fear of us. I don't know how many of them are in there, but I'm certain there are many more cowering in the town." She bent to pick up her sword. "We do not need the Trinovantes." She raised it high above her head. "Into battle, brave Iceni!"

They did not need a second invitation: the Iceni surged forward, their ferocious war cries joined by the crash and clatter of their spears and swords and the urgent call of their horns.

And as they poured into the centre of Camulodunum, they heard their own battle sounds echoed from across the town: with a glorious explosion of noise and the flash of armour and blue tattoos, the Trinovantes burst into the forum at the entrance opposite to the Iceni.

Brennus was in the front chariot, his hair flying, his sword held high and his face cracked into a huge broken-toothed grin. "Hail, noble Boudica!" he yelled, and the Trinovantes roared their support.

Boudica felt her heart swell with pride and quicken with the thrill of the battle to come.

"Onward, bold Iceni!" she shouted. "To battle, valiant Trinovantes!"

Then, shouting and chanting war cries, the Trinovantes wove their chariots in between those of the Iceni, lighting the wooden torches of the Iceni with their own already-lit stakes. In a mass of noise and fury, they converged on the town, and flung the flaming torches into the Roman buildings.

6

The First Battle

With a whoosh, the wooden buildings roared with flames and banged with explosions, and the air was thick with billowing drifts of smoke and smuts and sparks. The stone buildings heated up like fire pits, driving the Romans out like terrified ants.

Brennus jumped from his chariot, brandishing his sword. The look he gave Boudica over his shoulder was one of challenge.

"Perhaps you should stay up there – watch the action!" he called up to her. "Let the men defeat these Roman dogs!"

Boudica saw how his lip curled. Hadn't she already shown him she was his equal? She squared her shoulders. No, not his equal – better than he was.

She would not be outdone – not by any Trinovante, certainly not by a man, and especially not Brennus.

"We shall see how many heads the women bring home!" she shouted back.

Then with a loud battle cry, her mantle billowing behind her, and her sword held high, she leapt from her own chariot, and charged into the midst of the fleeing Romans.

The charioteers drove the chariots to the outskirts of the town, leaving the warriors to fight on foot. Swords slashing and armour glinting in the late afternoon sun, the Britons rampaged through Camulodunum. The hot air was filled with the shouting of the warriors and the screams of the Romans as they fought in the narrow streets. Boudica fought shoulder to shoulder alongside her people, dodging and parrying. Every thrust of her sword was her revenge for the pain that had been inflicted on the Iceni, her daughters and herself.

It wasn't long before the streets ran red. Dead Romans lay strewn about like discarded bundles of dirty washing. The cries and shouting became muffled moans and whimpering. While the flames had died down, smoke and ash still rose from the rubble, and the air was hot. Boudica wiped the blade of her sword on the robes of a dead Roman, and straightened up. Her back burned with pain, and her tunic was sticking to her skin where she'd begun to bleed again. She frowned. Where were her daughters?

"Camorra! Tasca!" she called, her heart quickening. Throughout the combat, she'd kept an eye out for them, making sure they were nearby, praying they'd be unharmed.

"Over in the forum, Lady!" a Briton warrior shouted over to her. He joined the groups of other Iceni and Trinovante fighters making their way back to their chariots, sweaty and smoke-blackened.

Raising her hand in acknowledgement, Boudica picked her way through the drifting smoke and over corpses towards the forum. She owed a thank-you to the gods, for the warrior was right: the girls were there, standing in front of the Romans' temple. Relieved, Boudica ran towards them.

"Mother!" Tasca called. "Are you all right?" She flung herself at Boudica, who put her arms around her younger daughter. Boudica was worried about her. Tasca was still deeply upset: she and her father had been so close, and she missed Prasutagus terribly. And she wouldn't forget the Roman's attack in a long time – if *ever*.

"Look!" Camorra shouted, holding a head up by the ear. "I'm going to tie this one to my horse!"

It was the head of the centurion who'd attacked Boudica's daughters.

"So we are avenged, my daughters." Boudica rested her hands briefly on their shoulders. "Go back to your chariot. I'll join you there shortly."

She watched as they left the centre of the town, then turned back to examine the temple more closely. Scorched by fire, yet surprisingly otherwise untouched, the temple rose as solid as ever amongst the rubble around it. The doors into it remained tightly shut. Boudica kicked at them, but they didn't budge. What had happened to the Romans who'd hidden inside? Was it possible that they were still in there? She knelt to put her ear to a barred window low on the ground. Could those scufflings be the sound of people?

Boudica got to her feet again. There could still be Romans hiding in there. Better check, she thought. She wasn't going to leave Camulodunum with any Romans alive.

As they didn't seem to have come out of the front doors, perhaps there was an exit at the back of the temple. Beating away the bitter smoke with her hands, she made her way round the building.

Strangled gurgling noises made her quicken her pace.

A centurion was bent over something in the middle of the broken stones and masonry. The gurgling sounds came from there. Another centurion was rummaging in the rubble.

Without making a sound, Boudica sprang closer. The first centurion was struggling to hold something – someone – down.

"Get on with it, Lucius!" he called to his mate. "He's a brute, and I can't hold him much longer."

"Almost – there – I've got something to beat him with. Keep your hair on, Flavius!" Lucius said, grabbing hold of a broken wooden beam.

Boudica was behind Lucius. Neither Roman had seen her. The man on the ground was familiar.

Brennus.

Pinned down, a thick Roman arm crushing his windpipe, Brennus's face was dark red as he strained to breathe.

Lucius raised the beam. Boudica grabbed it. She pulled it out of his grasp and flung it aside. Lucius swung round, his eyes wide with surprise. In that moment, Boudica drew her sword from her belt and brought it hard and flat against Lucius's arm. He staggered sideways. She leapt towards him, but he'd regained his balance. With his lips peeled back into a snarl, he grabbed her wrists, shaking her hand so that her grip on her sword loosened.

Rasping noises, meanwhile, were coming from Brennus. He couldn't last much longer.

It was kill, or be killed.

Boudica kicked out at Lucius, who let go of her, and in a smooth arc, she swung her sword at him, slashing his neck. He fell to the rubble and was silent.

Now for his companion, Flavius. He was still bent over Brennus. In one bound, Boudica was behind him.

"Flavius!" she shouted. "Over here!"

He looked over his shoulder, his mouth open. Once again, Boudica seized the moment, and dealt the Roman soldier one sharp stab to the back. He slumped on to the rubble, moaning a little, before he, too, fell silent.

Boudica leaned over Brennus. She nudged him with her foot. He stirred. So he was alive. He blinked a few times. Then with a hoarse roar, he stood up, reaching for his sword as he did so.

"It's all right," Boudica said. "I've dealt with them." She pointed to where the Romans lay.

"They were mine. You didn't have to interfere." Brennus's voice was gruff.

"Is that your way of thanking me for saving your life?" Boudica asked, angry. She marched over to the back of the temple, glancing over her shoulder at Brennus. "Perhaps you want to carry on with your little lie-down, but I need to move on – there's unfinished business here."

7

Message to the Romans

She saw at once that there were no rear doors to the temple, and no windows through which anyone could have escaped.

"What do you mean, 'unfinished business'?" Brennus asked. He'd come up beside her.

"There are Romans inside the temple," Boudica said. "Locked in. Hiding."

She made her way back to the forum. Briton warriors were moving back towards their chariots, laughing, chanting and shouting.

"Victory, Lady!" an Iceni man called out to her, holding up two Roman heads by their hair and shaking them.

"Almost," Boudica said. "But not quite."

Brennus appeared again with a group of Trinovante warriors. "We'll storm the temple," he said. Despite the red-purple bruise spreading across his neck, he was swaggering again.

"Lady!" Two Iceni warriors ran towards Boudica, dragging between them a Roman boy of about seventeen or eighteen.

Boudica turned towards them.

"Found him," one of the Iceni said. "Hiding over there. Shaking like a leaf. We were just going to kill him –"

"But we thought you'd want to do that," the other said, laughing.

Boudica saw how terrified the boy was. His eyes were wide, and his teeth were chattering.

"I have an idea," she said to Brennus. "Do not storm the temple yet."

Turning back to the boy, she said: "You have a choice. Either I kill you now – " she grabbed the handle of her sword. The boy flinched. "Or I let you go, and you take a message to your Roman commander. Tell him we are laying siege to your temple and the cowards inside it. Ask him if he is brave enough to come to Camulodunum to defend it." Boudica tapped her sword. "Have you decided?"

"Y-yes," the boy stammered. "I w-will go t-to P-Petilius C-Cerealis. Take him your m-message."

"He has two days," Boudica said. "If he does not appear within this time, the blood of your people will be on your hands."

Colour drained from the boy's face.

"Let him go," Boudica said to her warriors.

The Iceni loosened their grasp and the boy stumbled. He remained where he was for a moment, too shocked and frightened to move.

"What're you waiting for? Run, boy!" Boudica shouted. "Before I change my mind!"

The boy bolted, not looking behind him.

"What is the purpose of this?" Brennus asked, frowning. "Why wait two days? We can kill those Roman cowards right now."

Boudica smiled. "Of course we can. But look around you. Our people are full of the heat of battle. So I want to draw the Roman army here, now – " She swept her arm to indicate all of Camulodunum. "Draw the Romans in, and slaughter as many of them at once as possible."

Boudica felt a thrill ripple through her – the thrill of victory. She understood now how her husband, Prasutagus, had felt when he'd returned from battle, his limbs heavy, but his heart alive and quick with the smells and sounds of war. The gold torc was warm around her neck. She touched it lightly. It was her beloved Prasutagus who had made her bold and strong. She wouldn't let him down.

8

The Romans Advance

"The two days are up," Brennus said. He planted himself in front of Boudica's camp fire, his hands on his hips. His upper lip rolled back into a sneer. "Stupid plan of yours didn't work. That Roman boy didn't make it. No Roman army will come. And here we are just sitting about like chickens."

It was late afternoon. The air smelled of the fires that still smouldered in the remains of Camulodunum. The Britons were camped outside the town, waiting for Petilius Cerealis and his legion. Waiting to ambush him and his men.

"I'm giving the order now," Brennus said. "To storm the temple, and move on."

Boudica stood up. She glared at him. "You are too impatient. I have not yet heard from the scouts

51

I sent to seek out the Romans. I say we wait until nightfall."

"No." He took a step nearer. She could see the mottled blue and yellow bruising across his neck close up; she could smell the mutton on his breath. "Where are your eyes, woman?"

He turned to look at the massed Trinovante and Iceni people.

"Look at them." He waved his hand. "They're bored. Restless. The battle heat has gone cold. We need action."

Boudica glanced around. The people were grouped around fires, some of them pacing about. Not far from where she was standing, a man and a woman were arguing loudly. The whine and shriek of children were joined now and then by the barking of a dog and the whinnying of horses.

Brennus was right. It felt like a game of hide-and-seek that had gone on too long. If no action were taken soon, Boudica knew that their people would lose interest and wander off.

She drew herself to her full height.

"Any sign of the Romans in the temple giving in?" she asked.

"No. They must still have food and water in there." Brennus made an irritable noise. "I've had enough. We're going in. Now."

He turned to stride off. Boudica grabbed his mantle. He was not in charge, and she did not want her people to think that he was.

"Not so fast, friend. We do this together," she said. "Call for ten of your strongest. I'll see you at the temple with mine."

Brennus gave her one of his broken grins, and immediately began to summon his warriors.

Boudica strode deep into the Iceni encampment, picking out eight men and two women to storm the temple. They leapt to their feet to follow her, keen on action. Perhaps Brennus was right in his impatience to make things happen. Perhaps she had been wrong in waiting for the arrival of the Roman army.

She headed for her chariot.

"Lady – "

Boudica turned. One of her scouts was running towards her. It was Iaros. He stopped, panting, as he tried to get the words out.

"Lady – the Romans – they're advancing – "

She seized his arm.

"Advancing where? On Camulodunum? How far away are they now? How big an army?"

"Yes, Lady." Iaros struggled to catch his breath. "Advancing on Camulodunum. Some fifteen miles away south and west of here. Ninth Legion, I think. Numbering thousands. Beginning to set up camp for the night."

There was no time to lose.

"Lugubelunus," Boudica said to one of the warriors she'd chosen, a stocky man with muscle-roped arms and legs. "Go to the temple. Take command in my place. Tell Brennus the Romans are approaching. Storm the temple. Kill the Romans inside. Make haste."

She darted a glance over the encampment, feeling a mixture of thrill and fear. "I shall rally our people," she continued. "We shall advance to meet the Romans. You and the other Iceni warriors, join us when your task in Camulodunum is done."

"But – excuse me, Lady, for asking – but what about the Trinovantes?" Lugubelunus asked, waving his hand in the direction of their camp.

For a moment Boudica was uncertain. Some

of the Trinovantes had drawn near, curious about what Iaros had come to report.

"Are we to go with you?" someone called out. "Meet the Romans?"

"So the Romans are near? Let's harness the horses!" another shouted. "Into battle!"

Knowing that she should not take charge of them, Boudica raised her right hand. "Fellow Britons – " She had to shout to make herself heard above the growing hubbub. "Fellow Britons, I am glad of your support. But it is for your commander Brennus to decide whether or not to lead you into war. Wait for his return. It is his decision."

"I say we go with the Iceni!"

"Enough waiting! Into battle with Queen Boudica!"

Boudica was flattered. But Brennus would be angry.

"Bold Trinovantes – " She raised both arms trying to quieten them. "I say you should wait!"

"Lady?" Drawing up alongside in her chariot, Drustan called down to Boudica. One of her horses whickered and reared a little. "Your chariot is ready. Your daughters are already in theirs."

Boudica looked up. Already the sky was growing dark; a cold wind was sneaking through the camp, raising goose pimples on her arms and lifting her hair. We should move now, she thought, under cover of darkness. The forest was thickly wooded; it was well known to the Iceni. They could hide there. Surprise the Roman legion at daybreak.

She leapt aboard her chariot.

"All set, Camorra? Tasca?" she called out to her daughters in the chariot behind hers. The wind whipped their copper hair, and in the late afternoon light they looked surprisingly alike – pale skin, and cheeks reddened by the chill wind. There were still traces of terror in Tasca's face, but as she nodded at her mother, Boudica saw that her fear was mixed with determination.

"Yes, Mother!" Camorra shouted back, and knocked the Roman head hanging from the horse's neck with the tip of her sword. It swung like a horse chestnut.

"To battle!" Tasca called, glancing over at Boudica for approval.

Boudica laughed. "Let's go, Drustan!" she shouted.

Behind her she heard the rumble and creak and clopping and whinnying of chariots and horses, growing louder as more and more warriors joined the convoy behind her, and it made her heart swell with pride.

9

Massacre

Boudica woke long before dawn began to split the sky. The forest was damp and cold: she had banned campfires so as not to alert the Romans to their presence. She sat between her daughters, tucking their blankets around them, and wrapping her own around her shoulders. She wondered what the day would bring. Would they overcome the Romans? How many Iceni lives would be lost?

Her thoughts were interrupted by the arrival of another messenger, Seisyll, brought to her by one of her men.

"What news?" she asked, getting to her feet.

"Huge massacre of the Druids. Paulinus Suetonius – " Seisyll turned his head and spat on the ground. " – cursed Roman dog – advanced on Mona Island. By flat-bottomed boats and swimming horses."

"How many Britons killed?"

Seisyll bowed his head. "Every one, Lady, all slaughtered. Men, women, children. The sacred groves burnt to the ground."

"The entire island massacred?" Anger heated Boudica's blood. She threw down her blanket. "Right!" she said, pounding her fist in her hand. "We'll show them! Today we shall have our revenge. Thank you," she said to Seisyll, dismissing him.

So many times Prasutagus had spoken to her of the Romans' camps, and how she wished now that she'd listened. Pacing backwards and forwards, she held her head trying to remember his words. The layout was always the same, he'd said. Always a rectangle. What else? Something about a ditch on the outside, and then a kind of fence... and the general's tent in the middle? Was that what he'd said?

There wasn't any time to waste trying to remember. Calling her most trusted people, she laid out her plan. The Iceni were to be woken. They were to advance on foot in silence on the Romans' camp. There would be sentinels on guard – twenty of her most ruthless warriors would speedily deal with them. Then, the Iceni would creep amongst the slumbering Romans.

And kill them.

The Briton chariots, meanwhile, would, as usual, wait nearby. They would be ready to swoop upon the camp and, at her signal, to carry the Iceni warriors to safety.

Thick cloud had billowed up during the night. It cloaked the moon, and gave the Iceni the cover they needed. As soundlessly as possible, they left the forest on foot and moved over the rough ground towards the Roman camp. A band of warriors had run on ahead. Not long afterwards, one of them returned. He found his way to Boudica, the tang of fresh blood on his clothes.

"The Roman guards," he said. "All despatched in silence. The rest of the camp sleeps on."

"Thank you. I commend your boldness."

The warrior slipped away into the darkness. Boudica sent word that the Roman guards had been killed.

Moving more quickly, the Britons covered the ground to the Roman camp in little time. Boudica saw what Prasutagus had meant: they had first to cross a ditch. Once across that, they still had to get over the heap of soil that ringed the camp – soil that was studded with rocks and debris, and sharp wooden stakes.

The Briton warriors felt their way round the camp, the bodies of the murdered Roman sentinels marking the gateways into it. Now that the guards were dead, the Britons poured through.

The first wave of warriors moved like cats. Stealthy, moss-footed, they jabbed their spears deep into the hearts of the snoring Romans. The next wave and the next were less silent. Boudica noticed that the rowdiest were the Trinovantes. She tried to quieten the ones nearest to her, but, fired with fighting spirit, they swept through the Roman camp, roaring as they fell upon the enemy, slashing, stabbing, spearing.

Leaving the main fray, Boudica darted around the edge of the camp. It was organised into straight streets, with tents in strict rows. How orderly the Romans were. She was impressed, though she would never admit that to anyone. Where was the Roman commander, Petilius Cerealis? She wanted to get to him quickly: it was his head she wanted dangling from her horse's neck.

Keeping to the darkest shadows, but holding her sword ready, she dodged Roman soldiers blundering out of sleep. The warriors behind her would soon deal with them. The wind carried the smell of manure and hay. She wasn't far from where the horses were tethered.

Moving on, she saw the Roman standards, the poles the soldiers carried into battle. They'd been stuck in the ground. Each of them was topped by the image of an animal. The most important of them all was the eagle. Was that it, glinting gold in the dark? If she stole it, it would destroy the spirit of the Roman army.

Slowing down, she looked around. The clouds were thinning, and a scrap of moonlight shone through. No one behind her. Ahead, a single large tent. The commander's, perhaps. It certainly looked more important than any other. Her heart quickened. She was torn. What should she do first: grab the standard, or attack Petilius Cerealis?

She reached for the eagle-topped pole, knocking aside the others.

Voices – urgent voices – came from the large tent. Boudica froze. Then came a clatter. It sounded like weaponry.

This was her moment. She'd kill Petilius, then seize the standard. She leapt towards the tent, her sword gripped tightly in her hand.

Only to be jerked backwards by her hair.

"Not so fast, my friend." Brennus's hoarse whisper rasped in her ear. "We'll do this together."

Boudica whipped around, slashing her hair free of his grasp with her sword. Hissing with fury, she raised the tip of the sword to his head. "Do that again and I'll carve another scar in your ugly face!"

Brennus reared his head away from the blade. Screwing his eyes into slits, he gave a dry laugh, before flinging the hank of tawny hair he was still holding high into the air. He knocked the sword away from his face, and stepped forward.

"You led my people away from Camulodunum. Who gave you the right?" he snarled.

"Listen to me, Brennus." She dropped her voice as she leaned in closer to him. There was now only a whisker's breadth between them. She glared into his tiny black eyes. "I – "

She wasn't able to finish her sentence as a tall Roman dressed in full battle gear burst out of the tent, the purple cloak fixed at his shoulder rippling behind him. Petilius Cerealis. It had to be. He yelled a command to the soldier that emerged behind him, but Boudica couldn't make out the words: as the brawl of battle drew closer to them, the clash and shriek and roar were growing louder. The soldier dashed off, shouting orders.

Shoving Brennus aside, Boudica made for the Roman. He was sprinting towards the row of tents that separated his tent from the main area of the camp. He slipped between the tents, Boudica right behind him. Brennus was at her heels: she could hear him panting.

"I'll get him!" Brennus shouted in a loud whisper.

Boudica swung round. "No! He's mine!"

In those few seconds, the Roman disappeared.

"Damn you, Brennus!" Boudica said, pushing him aside again.

Emerging from the row of tents, Boudica glanced up and down the avenue. No sign of him. The smell of horse manure was stronger though. The mayhem of battle was drawing closer and closer, but above it, Boudica could just hear the horses whinnying and stomping.

She stepped out of the shadows.

Only to be struck at her temple and flung like a clod of earth to the ground. Her sword flew from her hand and skittered off. Four hooves thundered past, inches from her head. She pulled back. Just in time: hundreds more hooves followed. Their thud beat a tattoo that echoed through her bones. Churned-up soil spattered her face.

Cerealis, she thought. *Fleeing on horseback. Coward.*

"You didn't think he'd wait for you, did you?" Brennus's mocking voice was in her ear. He stretched out a hand to help her up. She whacked it away and scrambled to her feet.

If she couldn't get Cerealis, at least she'd grab the standard. Feeling slightly dazed after the knock on her head, she ran back through the line of tents.

Just in time to see a flash of purple and the glint of gold as Cerealis rode over the bodies of his people through a gateway, the eagle standard raised high above his head. His cavalry followed him, trampling the bodies further into the soil.

Boudica leaned against a post to catch her breath.

"Damn you, Brennus," she muttered, banging her fist against the wooden post. "Damn you."

She'd been so close, but thanks to him, she had neither killed Cerealis, nor captured the standard.

"So you lost him!" Brennus crowed, appearing at her side. "Your husband would've got him."

She swung round, at the same time reaching for her sword, only to find it wasn't stuck into her waistband as usual. She lunged at Brennus, bringing her fist up to his chin, but drew back at the last minute. If she'd had her sword, she would happily have sliced that jeering smile off his ugly face. "Yes. He would have," Boudica hissed. "But then he didn't have you holding him back."

Brennus dangled her sword in front of her. "Is this what you were looking for?" He tut-tutted. "Very careless of you to leave it lying around."

She grabbed it from him. "And you need to train your warriors to shut up. We'd have won the battle in no time if it hadn't been for them."

"Next time you'll think twice before taking command of someone else's army."

"I. Did. Not. Take. Command. Of. Your. Army." She spat the words out. "They decided to follow me." She gave a dry laugh. "They obviously prefer the leadership of a woman."

Brennus curled his upper lip into a sneer, but just then the shrill call of a carnyx rang out. Boudica replaced her sword in her waistband. "I haven't all day to spend in idle chat. My warriors need me." She swung on her heel, and ran off in the direction of the sound of the horn.

10
Now What?

Like an egg, the sky had cracked, and the sun was spilling through. The battle was over. Dead Roman soldiers – Cerealis's infantry – lay sprawled everywhere.

Boudica smiled.

She'd been right about Genovefa's vision. The goddess Andraste was on their side.

She touched the torc.

And the spirit of Prasutagus was with her.

Boudica stepped into the midst of her gathered warriors, leaping on to a boulder lodged in the soil. They sent up a huge roar that quickened her heartbeat.

"Hail, noble leader, Queen of the Iceni!"

"Victory, Queen Boudica!"

They cheered and whistled and blew on their

horns. Some stamped their feet and beat their swords against their shields.

Boudica lifted both her arms and stretched out her palms. Slowly, the clamour died down, but in their filthy faces she could still read the joy of triumph.

"Yes, my bold and brave countrymen, victory is ours. The Roman infantry lies all around us, cut to pieces. And we have so frightened their leader that he has scuttled off like a frightened mouse."

The gathered warriors laughed and cheered again.

Boudica took a deep breath and cast her eyes over her people. She rested her glance briefly on Lugubelunus, planted in front of her, solid as an oak; beside him, she recognised Elisedd, tall and stringy with his helmet of black curly hair, and Genovefa, frowning fiercely, so broad-shouldered and dependable. She looked at those she knew well, and those she did not. She was proud of all of them. She felt her voice catch in her throat, and for a moment she thought tears would fill her eyes.

"Thank you, Briton warriors. You have served the

memory of my husband well. You have served me well." She raised her voice: "Now the Romans have seen our strength and our ferocity, never again will they dare toy with us!"

She dropped her arms to her sides. It was time to return to Thetford, to her villa, or what remained of it, and time to get back to her life, whatever remained of that. The leaves were changing colour. By now, the crows would be jabbing their sharp beaks into the red apples that bejewelled her orchard. She tried to make herself care about that.

Her head bowed, she stepped down from the boulder and turned to walk away.

But her path was barred. Her warriors had linked arms and made a barrier. Boudica was startled. What did this mean?

"Let me pass!" she said.

"No, Lady!" they shouted.

Spinning on her heel, she found that her people had formed a circle around her. Someone began to stamp his feet, drumming out a steady rhythm. One by one, others joined him, until the Roman encampment rang with the beat. Boudica felt her heartbeat speed up again as she turned in the middle of the circle. Confused, and panicking a little, she frowned.

Lugubelunus broke through the human barrier. He knelt before her, and within moments the gathered Britons were quiet.

"Queen Boudica, I am a man of blunt words. May I speak?"

Boudica waved her hand in the air to indicate that he should stand. "I prefer blunt words. Speak, Lugubelunus."

"We shall not return to our homes." His jaw was set, and there was a steely gleam in his eyes. "Our work has just begun. Lead us south, Lady, where many more Roman necks – " he made a swishing gesture across his throat with his finger " – wait for our Briton swords."

It took a moment or two before his words sank in. Boudica looked once again at the gathered warriors. Many were nodding, agreeing with what Lugubelunus had said.

So they wanted her to lead them... to move south...

She heard the distant cawing of a rook, the scrape of a sword against a shield, a dry cough.

The crisp early morning air carried the sounds clearly to her ears. Her people were quiet, waiting for her answer.

Was this a good life for her daughters? She should take them home, back to the life they'd known. She thought again of her garden, her figs ripening, dropping unpicked to the ground; she thought of her loom, and the half-hearted weaving she'd begun after Prasutagus had died.

There was a rippling movement amongst the crowd. Someone was ploughing through, making his way to the front.

Brennus.

Shouldering a couple of warriors aside, he stopped right in front of Boudica, barely two metres away from her. His hands on his hips, he stared at her. She saw the challenge in his eyes, asking silently, but with a jeer: are you courageous enough to do this?

"Yes!" she heard herself shout, before she'd even realised that her mouth was open. "Yes! South – to Londinium!"

The Iceni roared their approval. "To Londinium! To Londinium!"

Boudica saw the cracked smile appear in the middle of Brennus's snarled-up beard, the curl of his upper lip.

"Then on to Verulamium!" she added, her voice hoarse. And again her people yelled, and blew their horns.

In the mayhem, Boudica took a step closer to Brennus.

"And are you man enough to join us?" she asked him, spitting the words right into his ear.

Brennus jerked, and for a moment Boudica thought he might strike her, but then he threw his head back and laughed. "You are as fiery as your hair." Scrubbing at his chin through his beard, he added: "I like that. And I owe you my life. Until I have repaid my debt, we shall fight the Roman dogs at your side."

So there was a shred of honour hidden somewhere in his rough soul after all.

Boudica tossed her head. "What are you waiting for?" she asked him, leaping back up on to the boulder. "To our chariots, bold Britons!" she shouted above the clamour. "And south to Londinium!"

11

Londinium's Burning

It was late afternoon some days later. The sun was pale, hovering in the sky after a day of gathering cold. Boudica sat at her fire with Lugubelunus, discussing her plans for the attack on Londinium. She'd appointed him her chief warrior. His fierce spirit, his strength, and his unwillingness ever to give up, made him a fighter in the mould of Prasutagus.

There was rustling, and the thump and crackle of footsteps on the forest floor.

"Iaros, Lady," Boudica's guard announced.

Iaros staggered towards her, his chest heaving as he struggled to breathe. He bowed.

Boudica leapt to her feet, motioning the guards to leave her and Lugubelunus with the messenger.

"Paulinus Suetonius, Lady," Iaros said, panting

out the words. "Advancing on Londinium."

"Suetonius, you say? That – the dog that slaughtered all the people of Mona Island?"

Iaros nodded. "Yes, Lady. The same man. An ambitious soldier."

"How big is his army? Does he expect us there?"

"I do not know the size of his army, but I have heard that it is not big – not as big as Petilius Cerealis's legion." Iaros took a deep breath. "He has heard that we destroyed it, and that Cerealis ran away."

Lugubelunus gave a hoarse cheer.

Iaros continued: "Suetonius is marching on Londinium to do battle with us there."

"Right," Boudica said, clenching her fists. "He won't be disappointed."

She paced up and down beside her campfire, thinking through what she'd just heard. She'd planned to attack Londinium in the dead of night, much as they'd attacked Cerealis's legion. But now that she knew Suetonius was expecting them, she'd rather they fell upon Londinium quickly and loudly and in daylight. Far easier, anyway, given the vast number of Briton warriors.

She looked at the waning sun. If they left now they'd arrive in Londinium just after sunrise.

She smiled. The Romans wouldn't know what had hit them.

"Lugubelunus, find Brennus in this forest," Boudica ordered. "Tell him to stir his warriors into action. And instruct Drustan, too. We are leaving for Londinium before the sun goes down." Turning to Iaros, she put her hand on his shoulder. "You have done well. Thank you. But before you leave, tell me all you know about the layout of Londinium."

Drustan brought Boudica through the woods and out on to the marshy ground on the outskirts of Londinium. She was a short way ahead of her daughters, Brennus, and the mass of Iceni and Trinovante warriors. She'd ordered them to be silent; she could hear only the clopping of horses' hooves and creak and grind of the chariots.

She stepped down from her chariot. A fine mist drifted in patches in the morning air. Boudica took a deep breath, feeling the dampness in her chest. She drew her mantle around her shoulders. Samhain, the beginning of the dark half of the year, would soon be upon them.

"Lull before the storm, eh?" Brennus drew up alongside her.

Annoyed that he'd disturbed her moment of peace, she snapped, "Yes," and clambered back aboard her chariot.

The massed Iceni and Trinovante warriors were now emerging from the forest. Boudica turned her chariot round to address them.

"Londinium lies ahead of us. We shall ascend the hill you see in the distance as silently as possible. Then, when I blow three notes on my carnyx, descend the hill bold warriors, and make as much clamour and noise as you can! Pierce the hearts of the Romans with terror, before we follow through with our Briton swords!"

Signalling to Drustan, she set off towards the hill. The horses' breath rose in plumes as they climbed it.

At the peak, she stopped a moment to take in the layout of Londinium. It was just as Iaros had described: two hills, with the river, eel-silver, twisting between them. The clusters of low wooden buildings on either side huddled near the water.

She felt the familiar flutter in her stomach – excitement and fear whirling like autumn leaves. Behind her, chariot after chariot joined her. The earthy smell of churned mud mingled with the warm smells of animal hide, damp cloth and horses' sweat.

Soon the crest of the hill was crowded with Briton warriors, and Boudica imagined how frightening they must look from below. Her heart leapt with pride and a sharp, fizzy feeling that was a kind of joy. Her daughters were in the chariot beside her. Camorra's chin was raised, her eyes gleaming with excitement. Tasca was staring straight ahead, gripping her sister's hand.

"Courage, my daughters!" Boudica called out to them. She touched the torc at her neck and smiled.

Then, raising her carnyx to her lips, she blew three long notes that rang like an animal's call in the still morning air.

A quick nod to Drustan, and they were off, barrelling down the hill, shrieking, roaring, blowing horns, yodelling, hooves thundering, all caught up in a clamouring, urgent stampede.

As they drew nearer, Boudica could make out

Romans. She saw them stop what they were doing, look up at the charging horde of Briton fighters, and scatter – just like ants from a disturbed anthill. Boudica found herself roaring like her warriors, her whole body from her head to her fingertips thrumming with the thrill of battle.

Brennus thundered past her, bellowing like a bull. He was making for a low building close to the foot of the hill, in front of which a bonfire had been lit. It had been abandoned by the Romans who'd been tending it. Brennus slowed down just enough to swoop down with one of the thick sticks all the Britons carried into battle, and dip it in the flames.

Boudica swept up beside him, and did the same.

"This town will catch fire like a summer forest!" she called out to him, enjoying the blast of heat from the bonfire on her face.

"Quicker than that!" he yelled back, grinning with all his broken teeth. And leaping from his chariot, he waved the flaming torch above his head, sending tiny glowing embers shooting out in all directions. "Into battle, once again!"

Running at full pelt towards the entrance of the building, he kicked the doors open. His voice from inside was muffled, and joined very quickly by the sounds of screaming.

All around Boudica, warriors were dismounting and swarming the town. She raised the torch high above her head, desperate to leap down and join the fray, but first she needed to make sure Camorra and Tasca were all right. Craning her neck, Boudica scanned the mass of emptying chariots. Through the moving bodies and brandished swords, she caught a flash of long red hair.

"Camorra! Tasca!" she yelled, her voice hoarse as she strained to make herself heard above the clash and clamour. "Tasca!" It was her younger daughter she was most worried about.

"I see them, Lady," Drustan said. "I'll watch over them."

Just then Brennus lumbered up to her, panting, three Roman heads swinging by their hair from his fist. He twirled them in the air a few times. Fresh blood sprayed Boudica's face. Irritated, she swiped at it with her forearm.

"I'll throw these in here," he shouted, tossing the heads into her chariot behind her, "so you can pretend you got them. Then you can stand there quietly, caring for your daughters without bothering to do any fighting!"

Boudica tightened her grip on the torch.

What was in this man's head? One minute he seemed in awe of her, the next he was goading her, jeering, and always that sly smile playing on his ugly face. Why did she have to keep having to prove herself to him?

"Get out of my way!" she growled. Leaping down from her chariot, she swept the torch through the air. Did a flame lick the snarled thicket of his beard? She wasn't stopping to find out.

She joined the Briton warriors charging through the town and hurled her torch into the middle of the huddled buildings. The fire gobbled the dry wood with a fierce hunger: it had been a long, hot summer. Around her the shrieking of Britons and Romans mingled with the spitting and roaring of the flames.

Boudica ran through the streets, dodging the rocks thrown by yelling Romans, slashing with her sword any of them that dared draw near to her.

Strange, she thought. Most of the Romans were women, or older men, or children. Where was

Suetonius? Where was the army Iaros had spoken of? Had the Romans left Londinium completely undefended, like Camulodunum – or was it an ambush? She caught glimpses of the glittering river, and across it, on the other side, more wooden buildings. Were they lying in wait there? She ran ahead of the throng to get a better look.

Footsteps behind made her swing round, her sword at the ready.

"So where is the Roman army?" It was Brennus again, a sneer on his face. "Your scout lied!" He spat. "Typical Iceni."

"Iaros is not a liar! The Iceni do not lie," Boudica hissed.

"Huh!" Brennus grunted.

She'd had enough.

"Listen, Brennus." She leaned towards him, speaking through clenched teeth. "The Iceni do not need you. I do not need you. So clear off back to your miserable, stinking burrow."

She spun on her heel and ran through the streets towards the river. Trap or no trap, she wanted to get to the other side. If Suetonius were there, she and her clan would destroy him in no time.

12

Over the Bridge

Reaching the riverbank, she saw immediately that there was a bridge joining the two parts of Londinium. Suetonius hadn't destroyed it as she might have supposed. After all the smoke, it was a relief to stand now for a moment near the water and breathe the cool, damp air that rose off it.

Then, turning around, she ran back down the narrow streets towards the heat of battle, the air becoming thicker and thicker with billowing smoke and spiralling smuts.

Spotting Genovefa, she waved at her.

"Lady!" Genovefa called. "Thanks be to Andraste – you are safe!"

"We must cross the river," Boudica shouted.

Genovefa leapt towards her, making for a gap in the building that burned between them.

Just then a huge wooden beam separated from the burning structure, and crashed to the ground, spraying flaming shards of wood. It narrowly missed Genovefa, who sprang backwards. All around them, the town was in flames. Genovefa's path was blocked.

"We must destroy the other half of Londinium!" Boudica shouted again. "I'm crossing the river. There's a bridge. Find Lugubelunus. Find a way through all this. Follow me. Bring as many warriors as you can."

She turned and, retracing her path, quickly found her way to the wooden bridge. It was deserted. Her echoing footsteps made a lonely sound. Beneath her the green-brown river ran fast. It made her feel a little dizzy. Behind her, one half of the town burned; ahead of her – who knew what?

As soon as she set foot on the other side, she made for the nearest building, hiding in the shadows. Surely someone must have seen her crossing the bridge. And yet the town was surprisingly quiet. It seemed empty. Where were all the people? More importantly, where were Suetonius and his soldiers? Was it going to be like Camulodunum?

Still hugging the shadows, she crept around the

sheds that lined the riverbank. There were signs that people had been there recently: a small fire, still smouldering; crates half-opened; tools lying around as if thrown down; an abandoned sandal...

Should she wait for Genovefa and her other warriors to join her, or should she slip further into this part of town on her own, find out what exactly was going on?

She looked over her shoulder. No sign of Genovefa yet. She edged forward, darting from one building to another.

Through the windows of the empty houses, the overturned pots, discarded clothing and children's playthings were more signs of people having left in a hurry.

But surely a Roman legion wouldn't have fled, too? Perhaps Iaros had been wrong. Perhaps Suetonius had never come this way.

Boudica stood still a moment. Silence. Not even a rook's caw. She moved on, unsettled, darting glances around as she went. Something wasn't right.

The further she strode from the river, the fewer buildings there were. And the stronger the stink of horse manure.

And then she trod in some. She bent to wipe off her sandal. The pile was crusty on the outside, but still moist in the middle. Not more than a day or so old.

And there was loads of it. All over the small field she was standing in. She looked at the ground around her. Although sun-baked, the earth bore the prints of horses' hooves in the fine dust.

Yes, Iaros had been right. The army had been here. They'd been, and they'd flown. "What cowards!" she said out loud.

A metallic clink broke the silence.

Boudica froze.

There were a couple of sheds not far from her. Nothing else close by. The sound could only have come from there. Gathering her mantle, she sprinted towards the ramshackle buildings. One of them was a blacksmith's forge, his tongs and hammers strewn about. The hearth was filled with ash. Boudica dipped her hands in it. It was slightly warm.

That sound again, followed by a scuffling noise. There was something, or someone, there.

Standing utterly still, Boudica heard breathing.

She moved her gaze slowly around the shed until her eyes fell on a coracle, leaning against the wall.

It was rocking very slightly. Making no sound at all, her sword drawn from her belt, Boudica moved towards it.

With a hefty lunge of her right foot, she kicked it away.

"Stay where you are, coward!" she bellowed, holding her sword like a dagger.

In front of her stood, a youth, a Roman, aged about twenty, thin, his face and tunic dirty, and the look of a stray dog about him – menacing and cringing at the same time. He glared at Boudica, his lips peeled back. Something flashed in his hand. A knife. Boudica swung her sword. His knife fell with a clatter to the ground, and with one smooth movement, she shoved him right up against the wall, the tip of her sword pressed into his neck.

His eyes were wide with fear, and his hands grabbed at the air.

"Be still!" Boudica shouted, digging the sword point in a little deeper. "Where is Suetonius? Where is his army of Roman cowards?"

The youth swallowed.

"Speak!" Boudica ordered.

There was a clink. She spotted a cloth bag tied to the youth's waist. It was heavy with coins and, by the look of the chain hanging out of it, jewellery, too.

With one hand, she ripped the bag from his waist and flung it away. The air glittered silver and gold and chinked with the sound of spinning money.

"Thief!" she growled. "Instead of joining the army, you stayed behind to steal." She leaned into him. "I've a good mind to deliver you to Suetonius myself!"

"N-n-no!" the youth stammered, his hands fluttering like frightened birds.

"Where has Suetonius headed, you despicable Roman wretch? Tell me!" She twisted the sword point.

"Verul –"

Something slammed into Boudica knocking her sideways. A split second later the youth slumped.

Staggering to right herself, Boudica took in two things: the youth was dead, and there was a man looming over her.

13
Facing the Legions

"Are you deaf or just stupid? Didn't I tell you to clear off?" she shouted. "He was about to give me valuable information, and you had to interfere!"

Brennus gave a dry laugh. "Is that your way of saying thank you?" The laugh died on his lips as he kicked something at her feet. "Perhaps you would have preferred having your skull smashed to pulp," he said.

It was only then that Boudica noticed the man lying on the ground. He was a thickset Roman, grubby like the dead youth. In his hand was a hefty hammer, and in his back a dagger.

"I heard your voice. So did he. I saw him creeping in here." Brennus pulled his dagger out of the man's body. He rubbed the blood off the blade on the man's thick black hair, and replaced the dagger in his belt. "So I got him before he got you."

Boudica felt dazed. So Brennus had saved her life. They were quits. She thought of Camorra and Tasca. Who would have looked after them if she'd been killed?

"Thank you," Boudica said quietly, bowing her head. Unlike him, she could be gracious.

"What was that?" Brennus said, leaning his ear towards her. "What did you say?"

"You heard!" Boudica said, glowering. She'd thanked him once, and that was enough. "But why did you kill him? I hadn't finished with him," she said, pointing at the youth lying on the ground. A spear was sticking out of his head.

"Agh," Brennus made an impatient noise. "Just in case." He paced about the forge. "So – no Roman army here. What next? Do we meander back to Thetford and Camulodunum victorious, and yet cheated of victory?"

Boudica stepped over the dead man. She touched the gold torc at her neck, and secured her mantle with the brooch Prasutagus had given her. "No," she said.

From outside there came the call of the Briton

warriors arriving from across the river.

"Lady?" Genovefa's strong voice boomed across the field.

"Here!" Boudica shouted back.

"Onwards, Britons!" Lugubelunus ordered, and the warriors let out fierce battle cries and sounded their horns.

It cheered Boudica to hear them, and gave her fresh strength.

"Neither to Thetford nor to Camulodunum," she went on. "I wasn't finished with that Roman thief, but I'd heard enough."

Stepping out of the forge, she faced the Britons massing in the field in front of her. "To Verulamium, noble warriors! To Verulamium!"

Three days had passed. Boudica and the huge band of warriors were aboard their chariots or on horseback once more. Behind them, Verulamium blazed like a second sunset.

"Good job!" Brennus called to her, punching the air with his fist as his chariot drew alongside. He gave his broken-toothed grin. "The town is now a bonfire, and not one Roman left alive!"

Boudica smiled. "We have destroyed Camulodunum, Londinium and Verulamium. The gods are truly with us!" She touched the torc at her neck. And the spirit of Prasutagus is with me, too, she said to herself.

Glancing over her shoulder at their people, she felt again a surge of pride. Her life in Thetford, with its endless, empty days, seemed so long ago. How could she ever go back to that? Behind her, some warriors were chanting a victory song, beating their armour to the rhythm. Others had been at the mead, their drunken laughter joining the clamour.

Yes, this was the life for her now. And for her daughters: Camorra was a true daughter of Prasutagus, loving every minute of it, and there was even a tinge of colour in Tasca's cheeks.

"They say Suetonius is greedy for power, and a bold and brave commander," Brennus said. "But we have only seen his footprints. He never stays to fight."

"We shall meet," Boudica said, lifting her head. "He and the trembling namby-pamby weaklings he calls an army will feel the blades of our swords before long. I have sent Iaros to find out where Suetonius is cowering." She looked at the darkening sky. "We'll shelter in the forest tonight. But as soon as I have Iaros's news, we'll seek Suetonius out and fall upon him and his lily-livered boy soldiers."

That night there was more laughter amongst the Britons gathered in the forest round their campfires. Boudica lay in her tent between her daughters, listening to the high spirits of the gathered Iceni and Trinovantes. Eventually, the sounds died down and she, too, fell asleep.

It was shortly after dawn when Iaros arrived. Boudica called for Lugubelunus and Brennus to hear what he had to report.

"Half a day's travel from here," Iaros said, as soon as he could catch his breath. "Suetonius and his Fourteenth Legion, together with men from the Twentieth Legion."

"How many?" Boudica asked, beginning to pace in front of her fire.

"I think about ten thousand, Lady."

"Camped or on the march?" Brennus asked.

"Camped, but preparing for battle – with us," Iaros said. "They have heard that we destroyed

Londinium and Verulamium. They want revenge."

"Ten thousand?" Lugubelunus gave a snort. "That's nothing! We outnumber them many times over. We'll mash them into the ground in no time." He threw his head back and laughed. "Our womenfolk can stand by and watch the fun!"

Boudica frowned. She stopped pacing. So the Romans were expecting them. A shiver snaked up her spine. This would be the big battle, the one the Romans had cheated them of in Camulodunum, in Londinium and then in Verulamium. Would they win as easily this time?

"Sound the horn! Call the warriors to action!" she ordered Brennus and Lugubelunus. "Have them line up in the field beyond this forest, where I shall address them. We shall head for the Roman camp straight after."

Brennus and Lugubelunus left her campfire, and before long the sound of the carnyx pierced the dawn.

Boudica went to wake her daughters, but stood a moment before she did so. There was something she wanted to do first, something Prasutagus had spoken of.

Making sure no one was watching her, she made her way quickly to the stream that ran through the forest. Kneeling on the damp earth, she scrabbled amongst the vegetation that grew along the water's edge. It wasn't long before she found what she was looking for. Uprooting the whole plant, she crushed it into a leather bag which she tied around her neck.

Then she made her way back to her camp and woke her daughters. She told them the plan.

"Finally!" Camorra said. "Finally, the Romans are going to fight a proper battle."

By the light of the campfire Boudica saw how her eyes gleamed. Camorra looked up into the branches of the pine tree that overhung their camp. For the first time Boudica saw what was dangling there: tied by its hair to a twig was the head of the Roman who'd attacked her and Tasca.

"We shall return," Camorra said, talking to the head and knocking it with the end of her sword so that it swung slowly. "And when we do, you will be joined by the heads of other Roman cowards."

Tasca's eyes were wide. She turned away and shuddered. "I wish Father were with us, Mother," she said to Boudica. "It's going to be a really big battle. I'm frightened."

Boudica put her arm around her younger daughter. "Don't be, my child. Even though your father is not with us in person, he is with us in spirit. I feel it in my heart," she said, placing her palm on her chest. "Stay close to each other, and close to me."

She put her arm around Camorra, too, and together they made their way through the forest towards their chariots.

Her daughters on board their own chariot, Boudica had Drustan drive along the line of waiting Britons. They fell quiet when they saw her.

"Britons," she called out, raising her right arm, "We are about to face a great battle. The Romans await us, fired up with revenge for what we did to their towns. But they haven't yet felt the full heat of our vengefulness. You, Trinovantes, have not forgotten the battle at Gryme's Dyke, nor have you forgotten how the Romans seized control of Camulodunum. The stripes on our Iceni backs are still raw."

The warriors nodded, some shouting out:

"That's right, Lady. We haven't forgotten."

"We outnumber these Roman cowards. They hide behind their helmets and breastplates, trembling with fear."

"Boo! Roman cowards!" some of the warriors yelled.

"Onward bold Britons! We shall conquer them, or die with glory!"

The roar of their cheering filled her ears and quickened her heartbeat. This would be a battle to remember.

14

The Last Battle

Boudica and Brennus's chariots entered the plain side by side, the rest of the Briton horde in a mass behind them. Once again, Iaros's directions had been perfect: there were the hills on either side, and in the distance, the dark green of woodland. Ahead of them the Romans were waiting. Their armour glittered in the afternoon sunshine.

"Fodder for magpies, they are," Brennus shouted across to her. "Shiny as baubles. And just as useless."

Boudica smiled, but she felt a tightening in her stomach. The thrill of the battle to come – or fear?

As they drew nearer, Boudica saw that the Romans had arranged themselves in orderly lines, straight and neat like their streets. Behind her, the Britons were chanting and shouting and beating their shields and blowing their carnyxes, chariots surging forward in no particular order, horses' hooves hammering the dry earth.

Boudica touched Drustan's arm and he slowed her chariot. Brennus slowed, too. Behind them, the warriors quietened, and they, too, reined in their horses.

This was it.

The moment before battle.

Touching both her brooch and the torc, Boudica lifted her head to the open, blue sky and sent up a prayer.

Then, after sounding three long, high notes on her carnyx, she flung her arm high.

"Into battle, noble Britons!" she shouted. "To victory!"

Drustan spurred the horses on. Alongside her, Brennus thundered towards the Romans, her daughters not far behind.

"They're approaching!" Boudica called out.

As soon as they were within range, Boudica gave orders to slow the chariot and began to launch her spears. Around her the Britons were doing the same, hurling them in every direction, while the Romans rushed forwards, charging with their javelins. The air rained long sharp needles.

Using her shield to deflect the missiles flying in every direction, ducking and crouching, Boudica was just in time to see one of her messengers about to receive a Roman pike in his back.

"Seisyll!" she screamed.

He swerved, but as he did so, a javelin pierced his neck. The force of it flung him over the side of his chariot, on to the ground and under its wheels.

The air was torn by hoarse screams and the shrieks of terrified horses. The Romans kept advancing, volleys of arrows flying from the archers' bows. The Britons were trying to fight them off.

"Lady!" Lugubelunus roared at Boudica. His eyes wild, he leapt on board her chariot, knocking her down. He flinched again and again as his back took the brunt of the ten arrows meant for her heart. And then he slumped, completely still.

"Thank you, friend," she whispered, tears springing to her eyes. But this was not the time to mourn. Pushing Lugubelunus's body off her, she knelt beneath her shield, launching spears in every direction.

"Keep moving, Drustan!" she shouted. "Find my daughters! I want them here with me!"

Drustan drove the chariot, swinging one way, then another. Finally, the horses reared, jolting the chariot to a halt.

"Can't move, Lady!" he yelled. "But I see them ahead!" He pointed.

Boudica leapt to the ground, jamming her spear into the chest of an attacking Roman as she did so. Arrows whistling past, she dodged and darted, slashing with her sword, jabbing, parrying, piercing. A pike gashed her leg. She felt nothing as she shook her leg free.

"Camorra!" she yelled, trying to keep the flash of the girls' red hair within her sights. "Tasca!"

A Roman soldier planted himself in her path, his dagger raised, a smile on his narrow face. She lunged at him with her sword. He fell at her feet, gasping.

Boudica dodged more Roman blows, all the while searching for her daughters. Her heartbeat hammered in her ears, blotting out the battle cries and clashing and screaming and whinnying.

Where were Camorra and Tasca? Were they

together? Tasca would be terrified. What had she been thinking bringing them into battle? Why hadn't she left them in Thetford?

"We're... trapped!"

Someone caught her by the arm. Brennus. His cheek had been ripped open. Blood poured out. But it was the look of lost hope in his eyes that was more disturbing.

"No way through... ahead or behind," he said. There was defeat in the slackness in his shoulders, and in his slow, muffled voice. "Blocked... by our own chariots... by the womenfolk come to watch the... fun." He stumbled, and it was then that Boudica saw the sword that had been jammed in his back. "Run, Boudica. We're... doomed."

He fell against her, and she tried to hold him up. A rattle came from the depths of his chest. Then he slumped, and Boudica could no longer support his weight. She lowered him to the ground.

"Brennus!" She shook his arm.

He didn't reply. He couldn't.

"Goodbye, brother-in-arms," she said, crouching for a moment beside his body.

Then the roar of battle woke her from her daze,

and she leapt to her feet. Her daughters. She had to find them. She began to run, her eyes darting here and there, hardly taking in the dead and dying Britons, the charging Romans, and the never-ending spears and javelins and arrows.

"Tasca! Camorra! Tasca!" she shouted, their names merging into one long moan. She tripped over a heap of corpses. Could her girls be amongst them? The thought made her stop suddenly. An arrow stung her arm, sticking in her flesh like a gigantic bee sting. Boudica didn't pluck it out, didn't even notice it.

No, no, no. They couldn't be dead, couldn't be dead. Not dead.

"Camorra! Tasca!" she yelled, running again, and lashing out with her sword at any Roman who approached her. "Camorra! Tasca!"

"Mother!"

The high-pitched scream reached her ears through the thunder of battle. Boudica stopped again. Had she imagined it?

"Mother! Where are you?"

Hardly daring to hope it was one of her girls, Boudica sprinted in the direction of the voice.

It was coming from underneath an overturned chariot.

"Mother!" Camorra called out again.

Boudica saw her face appear. Checking no one was watching, Boudica darted to the chariot and slipped beneath it, snapping the shaft of the arrow in her arm.

"Camorra! Tasca! You're both safe!" She grabbed both of them and clung to them as best she could in the cramped space.

Tasca was rigid, her face white and stretched with horror. She stared at Boudica without seeming to see her.

"What happened?" Boudica asked Camorra.

"Oh, Mother, it was horrible. We lost sight of you. A Roman soldier grabbed Tasca."

She swallowed.

"He grabbed her neck, Mother. She couldn't breathe. I tried to fight him off, but then a soldier charged at me. And I couldn't fight both. But Drustan – Drustan – "

Now she began to sob. "He saw what was happening. He threw his spear at the soldier hurting Tasca, then he tried to drive the chariot

104

towards us. But a javelin – went into his chest. Arrows hit the horses. The next thing I saw – the chariot was upside down. I stabbed the soldier and I took Tasca's hand and we ran over."

Burying her face in her hands, she started to shake. "But the horses weren't dead yet. They were making a terrible noise. And – and Drustan was trapped. He wasn't dead. But he was in pain. He begged me, Mother."

"Begged you?" Boudica said, beginning to understand.

Camorra nodded. "Begged me to kill the horses... and him." She took her hands away from her face. Her eyes were wide. "I couldn't, Mother. I couldn't kill him. I had my knife ready. He was crying with agony. But I couldn't do it." She paused a moment, then she whispered: "Tasca did it." And she pointed to his half-visible body near to where they were crouching.

Boudica pulled both girls to her again, wetting their hair with her tears – tears for her daughters' suffering, and for the loss of Drustan.

After some time, she peered through the spokes of a chariot wheel. The battle had begun to die down; the ground was littered with bodies.

She took a deep breath. The air was heavy with the sweet-metal stink of blood, sweat and churned earth.

Romans were rounding up Britons. There were few left alive. Two soldiers were moving towards their hiding place, kicking bodies as they went.

Boudica knew without the whisper of a doubt that she would be the Romans' greatest trophy. Three trophies, with her daughters. The Romans would parade them through the streets of their towns, they would mock and jeer at them, whip and flog them, and then kill them in the most cruel and painful way possible.

If they were found alive, that is.

There was no time to lose. She snapped the leather bag free from around her neck.

"What's that, Mother?"

Boudica opened it, and took out the plant, crushed, but still green with the damp resin smell of the forest clinging to it.

"Hemlock."

"Poison?" Camorra gasped.

Boudica nodded.

Out on the battleground, one of the soldiers called out to the other: "I saw their queen not long ago. Alive. Six feet tall, red hair down to her knees." Boudica saw him jab some of the dead Britons with his spear. "She's here somewhere. I know it," he growled. "She's mine. And when I get her, I'll be handsomely rewarded."

A shiver snaked up her spine.

"They're coming," Camorra whispered. "I'm scared, Mother. So scared. There's nowhere for us to run. We can't get away."

Tasca burrowed into Boudica's side.

Boudica took a deep breath. It was definitely the right time. She broke the plant into three, and held it up to the light.

"Don't be scared, my beloved daughters. We can escape them."

Camorra grabbed two of the pieces of hemlock. "Now, Mother. Let's escape now." Stuffing one piece into her mouth, she handed the other to Tasca who hesitated only for a split second before doing the same.

Boudica was so proud of her brave and beautiful daughters.

"The two of you are the blessings of my life. You have brought me nothing but joy and delight," she said, tears filling her eyes. Bending over, she kissed the top of each girl's head. "Let's join hands." She took their hands in hers. Tasca was shivering. "Together we shall travel to your father – my dear husband, Prasutagus – who is waiting for us. Soon we shall be with him." She, too, placed the plant in her mouth and chewed.

They lay down, Boudica between them, the girls' hands joined across their mother's body. They all closed their eyes. Images passed across Boudica's mind, images of the battles, her faithful warriors and servants, Lugubelunus, Drustan, Iaros, Genovefa... the villa in Thetford, warm sunshine pouring over it like honey... and Prasutagus stepping out of the doorway to greet her and their daughters, his mouth open in greeting and his arms held wide.

Also available...

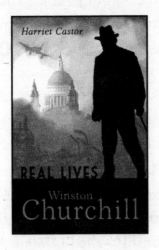

From soldier to MP to international war correspondent, Winston Churchill always has to be at the centre of the action. But following a turbulent career in politics, Churchill is faced with the worst war the world has ever seen. And this time, *he's* in charge.

Real Lives are narrative accounts of the life and times of some of the world's most iconic figures.

ISBN: 978-1-4081-3117-6
RRP: £5.99

1

War in Africa

Boom! Bang! The explosions were terrifying. Enemy soldiers, hidden in the hills beside the railway track, were firing on the train with rifles and big field guns.

"It's an ambush!" yelled Captain Haldane from his wagon. "Driver – go faster!"

The train – full of British soldiers in open-topped armoured trucks – raced ahead. It was crossing Natal, a British-held area in South Africa. The year was 1899 and a bloody war was raging between the British and the Boers – Dutch-speaking settlers who had lived in South Africa for several generations.

The railway track led downhill. Helped by the slope, the train was now going very fast. In one of the rear trucks, a newspaper war reporter stood among the soldiers. He turned to Captain Haldane. "We're going too fast, aren't we? It's unsafe. Should I climb along to the engine and tell the driver to slow down?"

Before Haldane could reply, there was an enormous bang and jolt from the front of the train. Everyone in the truck was thrown to the floor.

The newspaper reporter was the first to scramble to his feet. Quickly he climbed up to look over the side of the truck. The train was now at the bottom of the hill. On the grassy slopes above, he could see enemy soldiers running closer. The next moment heavy rifle-fire began whistling through the air and clanging against the steel-plated sides of the train.

"We're sitting ducks!" exclaimed the reporter, jumping back down. He turned to the army captain. "I'm at your service, Haldane."

Captain Haldane knew this man: though he was a war reporter, he'd been trained as a soldier. He and Haldane had been stationed together in India and Haldane trusted him completely.

"Find out what's happened to the front of the train," said Haldane. "See if you can clear the line. I'll organise the men at the back here to return fire."

The reporter obeyed immediately. He pushed his way out of the truck and ran down the length of the train. Bullets screeched overhead. He found the engine still on the line. But in front of it, two trucks had been derailed and were lying across the track. Ahead of them, another truck had flipped over completely. Some of the men who'd been riding on it were obviously dead; others were badly injured.

The reporter checked the track. The reason for the crash was clear: the Boers had put a rock on the line.

"I'm getting out of here!"

The reporter whipped round to see who had spoken.

"I'm a civilian! What am I paid for? To be blown to bits?" It was the driver, staggering from the engine, his face streaming with blood where a piece of shrapnel had hit him.

If we lose him we're doomed, thought the reporter. *He's the only man who knows how to drive the train.*

As the driver stumbled past, the reporter caught him by the elbow. "Think – no one's ever hit twice on the same day, are they?" he said. "Do your duty now and you'll get a medal for gallantry – you may never get the chance of one again!"

The driver stared. Who was this man?